The Magic Mirror Book

devised and illustrated by MARION WALTER

Story Link®
Program

SCHOLASTIC INC.

New York Toronto London Auckland Sydney

ISBN 0-590-41539-5

12 11 10 9 8 7 6 5 4   0/9

Printed in the U.S.A.   08

To my niece Rachel

who likes puddles

Can you see the whole moon?

Make two boats far apart

Now bring them close together

Can you mend the plate?

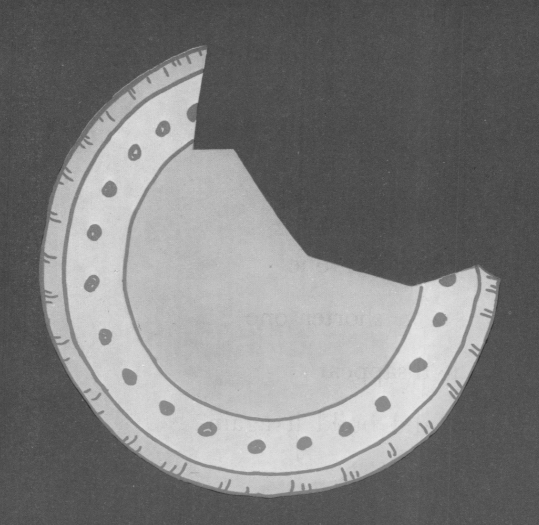

Build a taller tower

a wider one

a shorter one

Make it disappear

and build it again

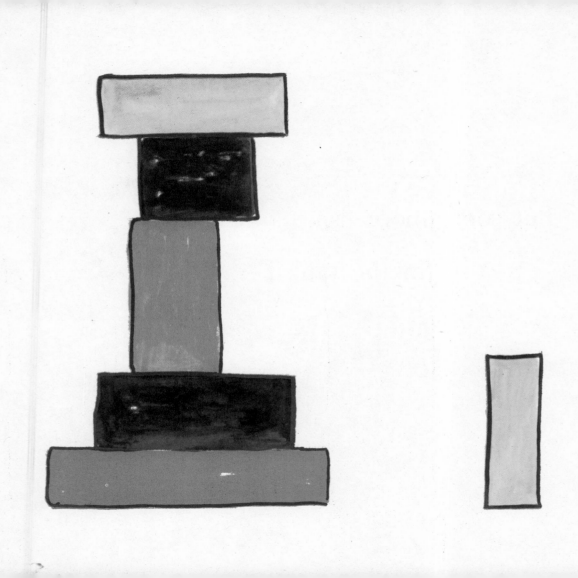

Put some more fish

in the tank

Make a bigger puddle

Make a smaller one

Make a longer worm

Make a shorter one

Make it disappear !

Can you see

another row of houses ?

Can you make longer stripes?

What else can you do?

See what you can make

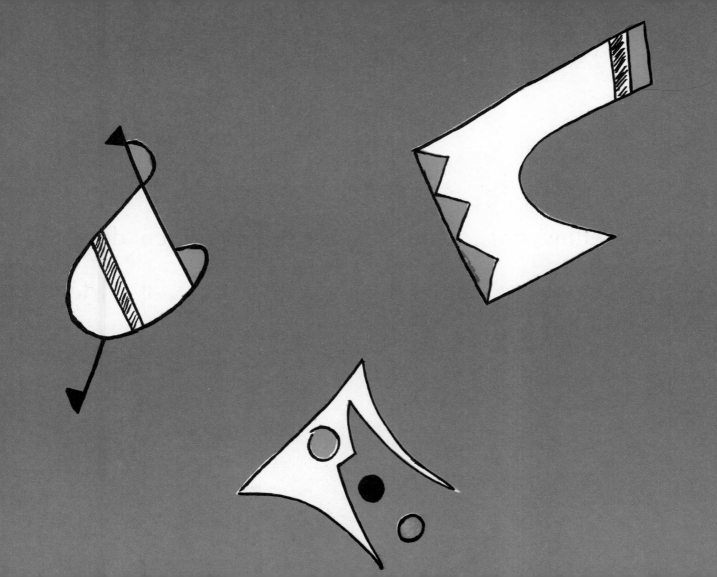

Yellow dots, blue dots, red dots, green dots

Ten dots, nine dots, eight dots, . . . two dots

Many dots or few

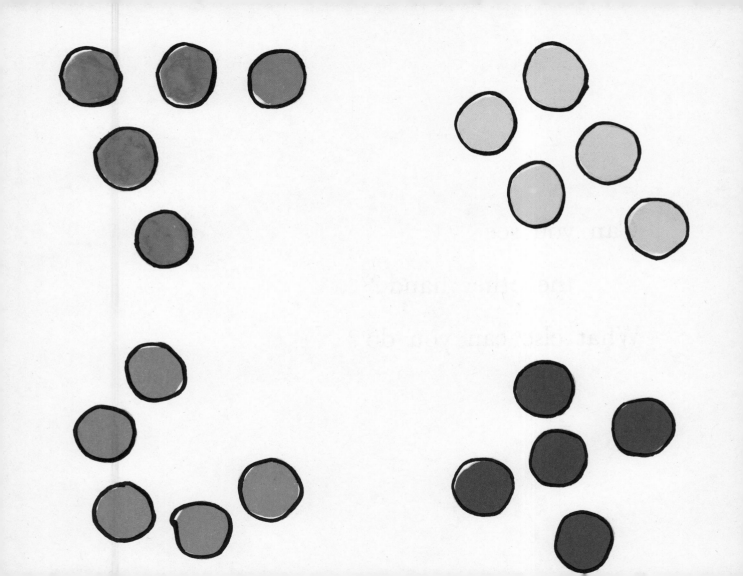

Can you see

the other hand?

What else can you do?

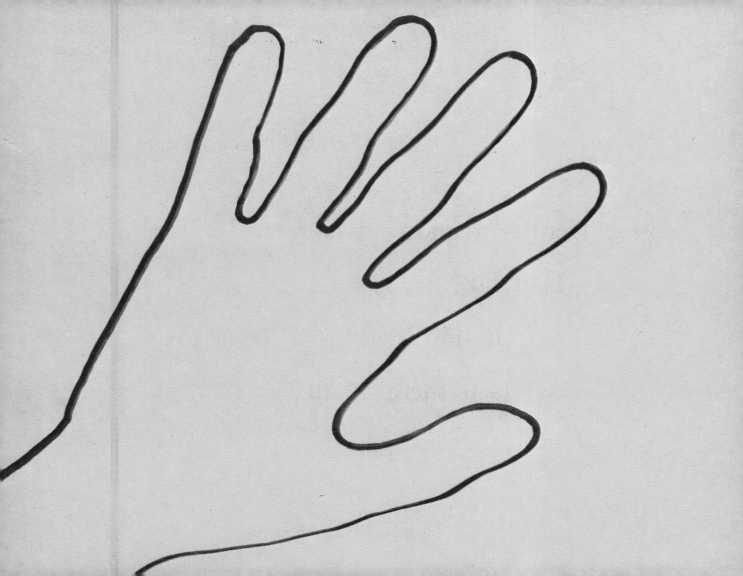

Here is a ghost

Is it fat?

Is it thin?

Is it there at all?

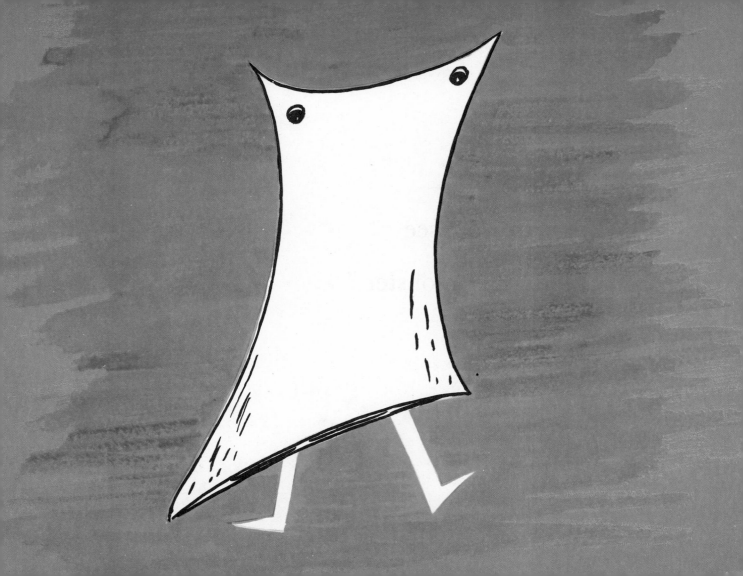

What can you see

in this monster ?

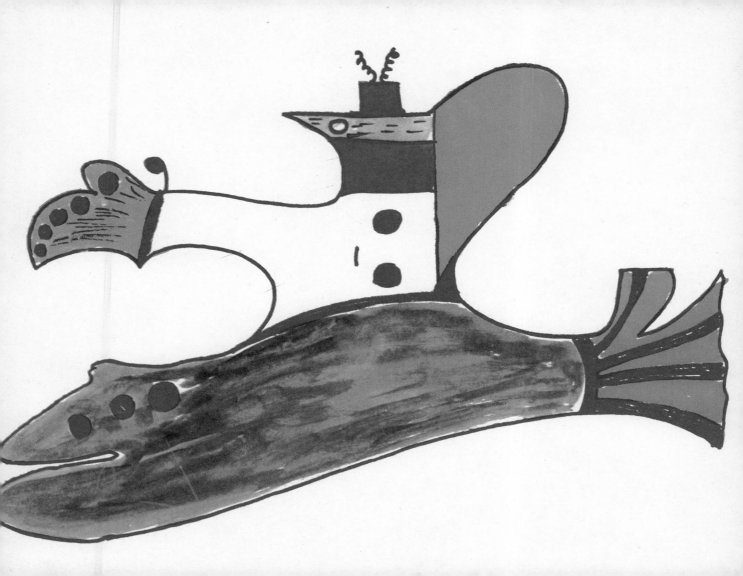